COMB YOUR HAIR

DRINK YOUR MILK

BRUSH YOUR TEETH

HANG UP CLOTHES

PUT TOYS AWAY

SHOES IN PLACE

Re-visions

Re-visions

Marcia Resnick

The Coach House Press Toronto 1978

Copyright ©1978 Marcia Resnick

Edited for the press by Stan Bevington.

Set in Venture Script and printed in Canada
in an edition of 5000 copies at
The Coach House Press
401 (rear) Huron Street
Toronto, Canada M5S 2G5

ISBN 88910-080-2
LCCN 77-83724

Special thanks to Laura Rubin and Amanda Rubin.

Also to Stan Bevington, Maxwell Blagg, Victor Bockris, William Burroughs, Richard Brodowski, Jay Burnett, Laura Cavestani, Bea Feitler, Kenny Florendo, Allen Ginsberg, Lili Golendorf, James Grauerholz, Maxine Groffsky, Bobby Grossman, Fayette Hickox, Linda Anne Hoag, Jessica, Betsey Johnson, Pooh Kaye, Lar, Annie Leibovitz, Erica Lennard, Little Johnny, Little Punch, Joe LoGiudice, Tom Main, Tessa Marquis, Simona Morini, Michael Oblovitz, Michel Odere, Amos Poe, Robert Projansky, Ratso, Don Rodan, Miguel Sanchez, Mike Stein, Michael St. John, Terry Southern, Kenny Tisa, Andy Warhol, William Wegman, Bud Werdenschlag, Henry Winkler, everyone at The Coach House Press and the Creative Artists Public Service Program.

Cover graphics by Ernie Thormahlen and Marcia Resnick.

Distributed by Rizzoli International Books.

To Humbert Humbert

She learned about morality at an early age. Innocence gave way to Good and Evil... everything appeared to be black and white.

She always drew the same picture — a blond oriental lady standing on a stage.

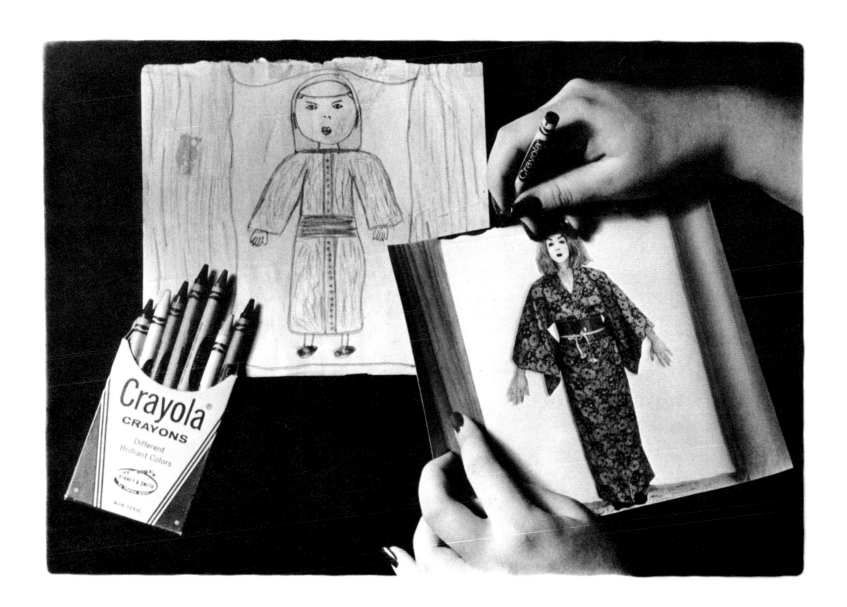

She played with her slinky toys and wore banana curls
and played with her banana curls and wore her slinky toys.

She would chew gum until the sugar ran out
and then stick it under her seat.

In class, one day, she was bitten by a mosquito and became unruly. Her teacher made her stay late after school.

She was forced to spend long hours watching walls
in order to redress her wrongdoings.

She was horrified to learn that she had been walking around school all day with her skirt hiked up in the back.

When she played the beautiful flower in her school play,
she memorized her lines perfectly but forgot when to say them.

*Inspired by a visit to the United Nations,
she painted her favorite doll black.*

She derived great pleasure from dressing her boy dolls in the undergarments of her girl dolls.

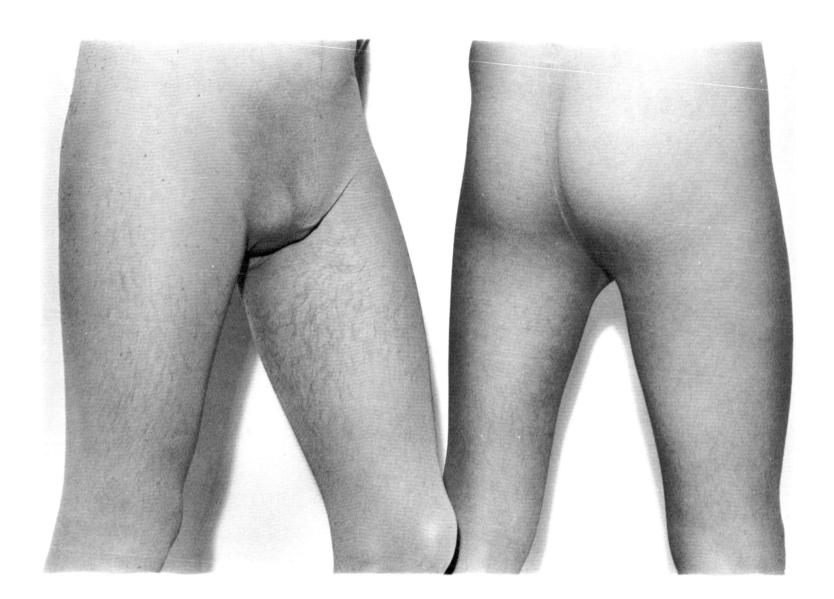

She was repeatedly told to stop looking at her feet while in the company of adults.

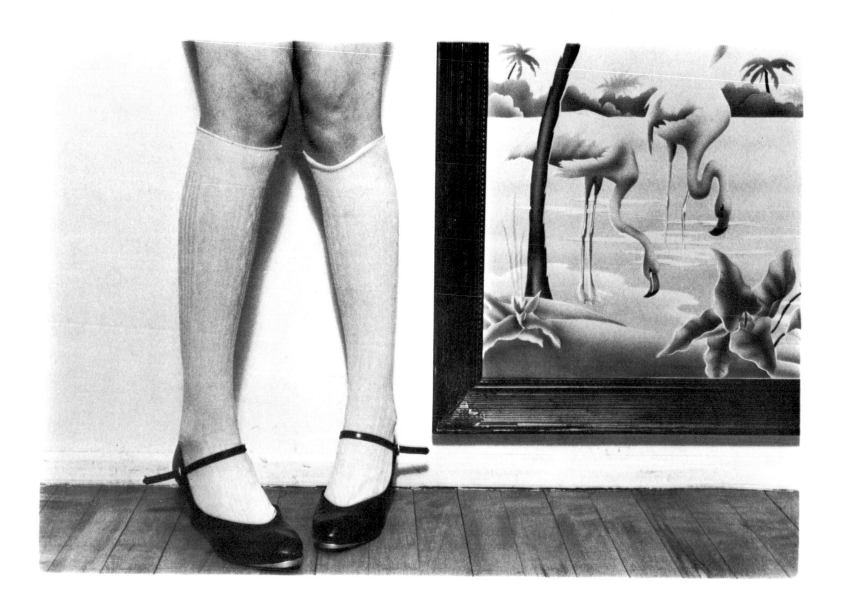

She was mortally afraid of clowns.

She would sneak licks of icing before blowing out the candles on her birthday cake.

She had a poor sense of direction and would awkwardly miss her mark when playing pin-the-tail-on-the donkey.

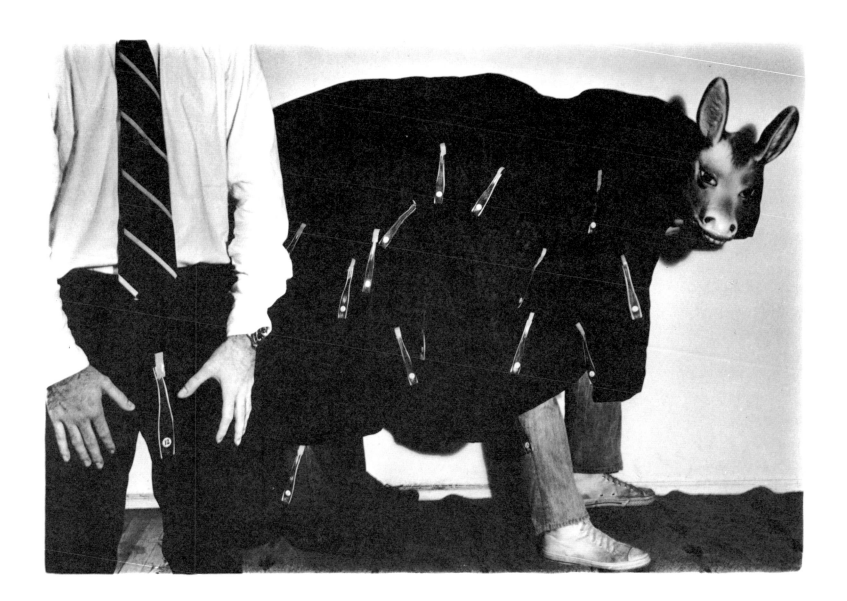

She couldn't grasp the logic behind table manners.

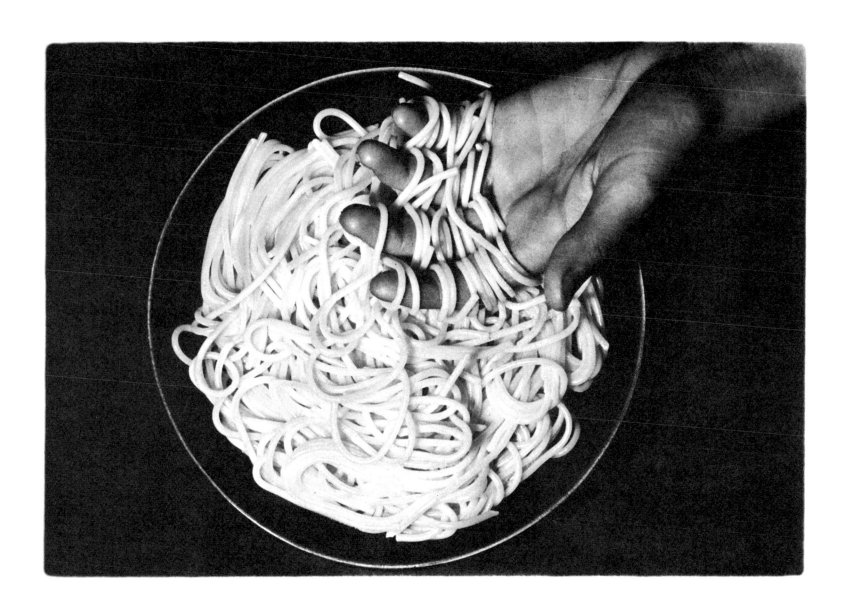

"Fingers are like forks," she would say and persist in eating with her hands.

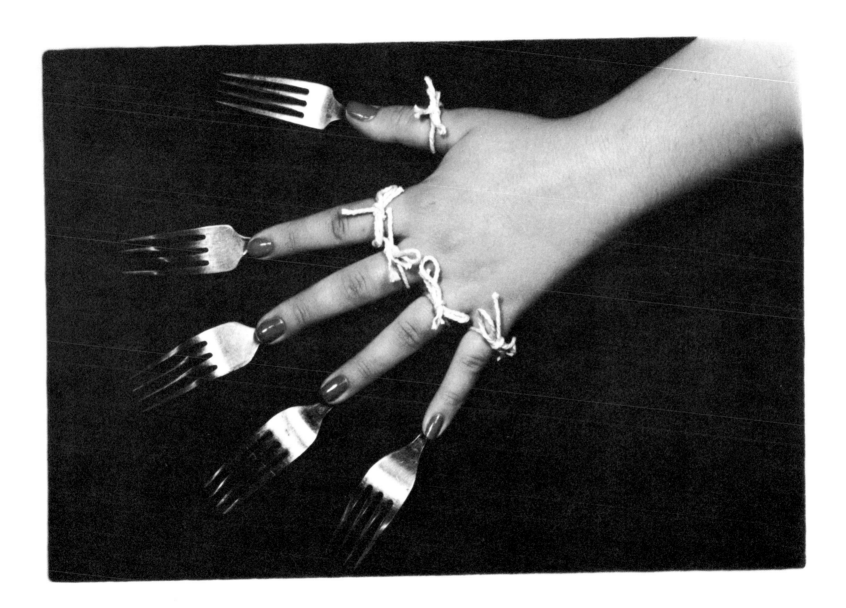

She became an expert shoplifter.

She enjoyed making loud noises in quiet places.

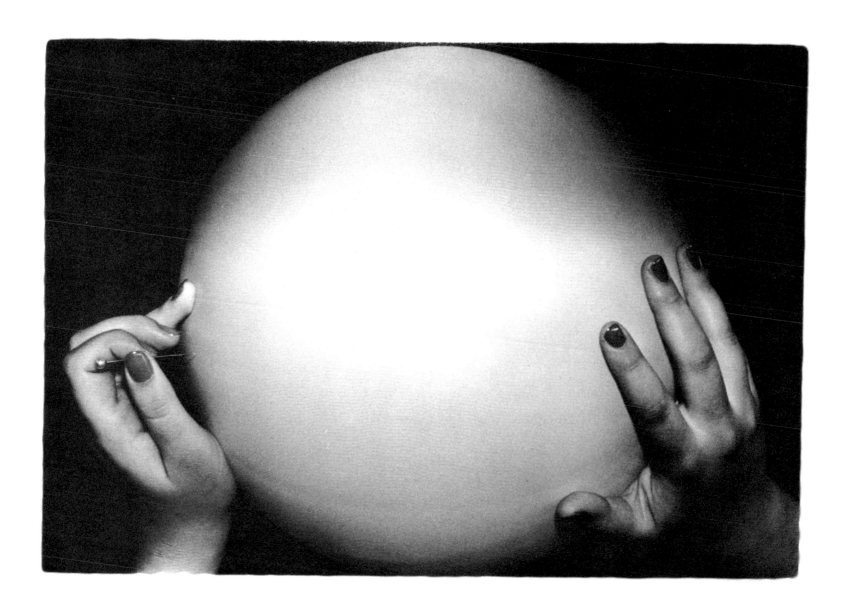

She painted racing stripes on her hula hoop in hopes that it would go faster.

While playing with her toys, she entertained cowgirl fantasies.

She was often gripped with the desire to be elsewhere.

On hot summer nights she would refresh herself by staring at the mural on the living room wall.

She would also gaze out the front window of her house
and watch the sinking ships rocking back and forth on the bay.

She couldn't sleep unless she was thoroughly tucked in.

By placing fake teeth under her pillow, she would collect extra money from the tooth fairy.

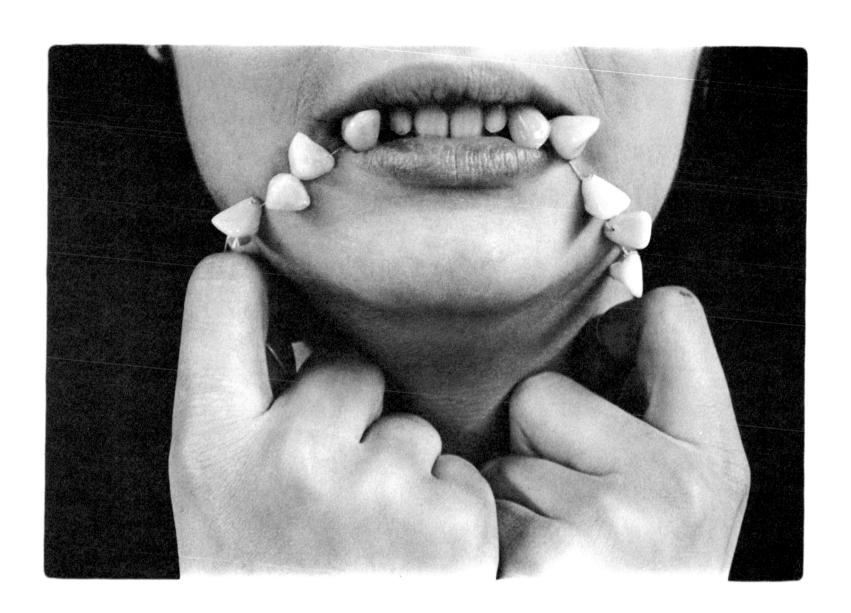

At late hours, she would quietly build a tent with her sheets and read stories with a flashlight.

She would rendezvous in her bed with the sandman every night.

She would often pass the shopping bag woman. One day the woman stood up, dropped her blankets and revealed her manhood.

She first learned the facts of life from a friend while on a class trip
to the bread factory.

Thereafter, she would break out in peculiar rashes and lose her voice when eating certain foods.

She secretly lusted for her television idols.

In her drama club, she would re-enact scenes from violent movies.

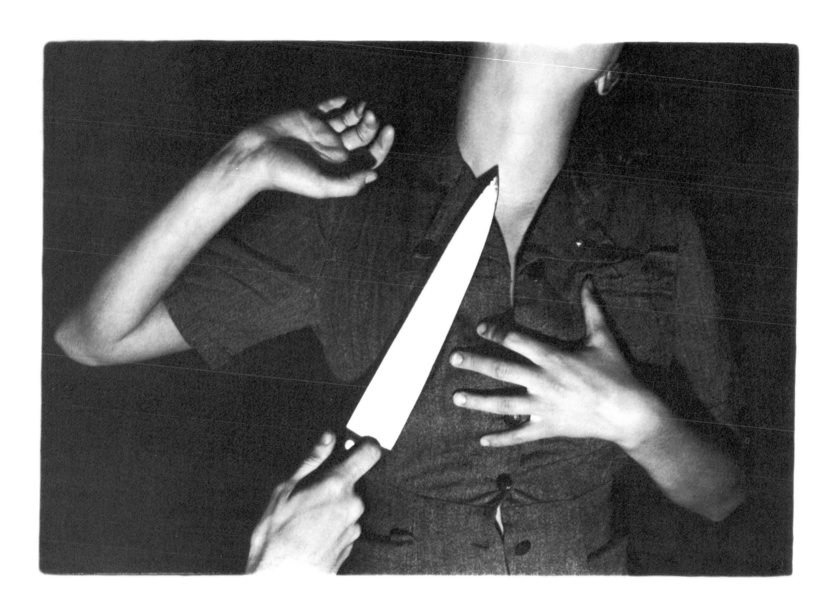

She would accompany her father to his National Rifle Association meetings where all of the fathers would show off their guns.

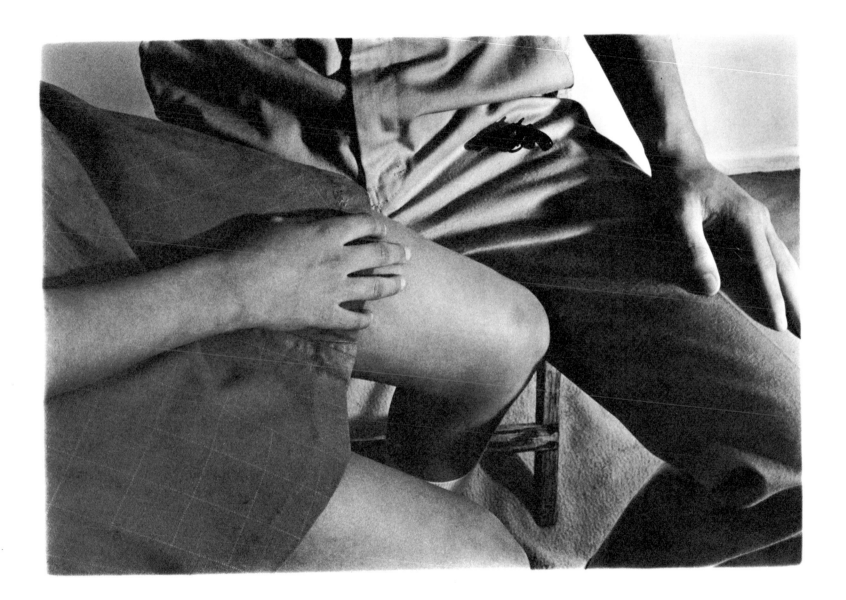

Not wanting to be publicly kissed by a boy, she avoided games of spin-the-bottle.

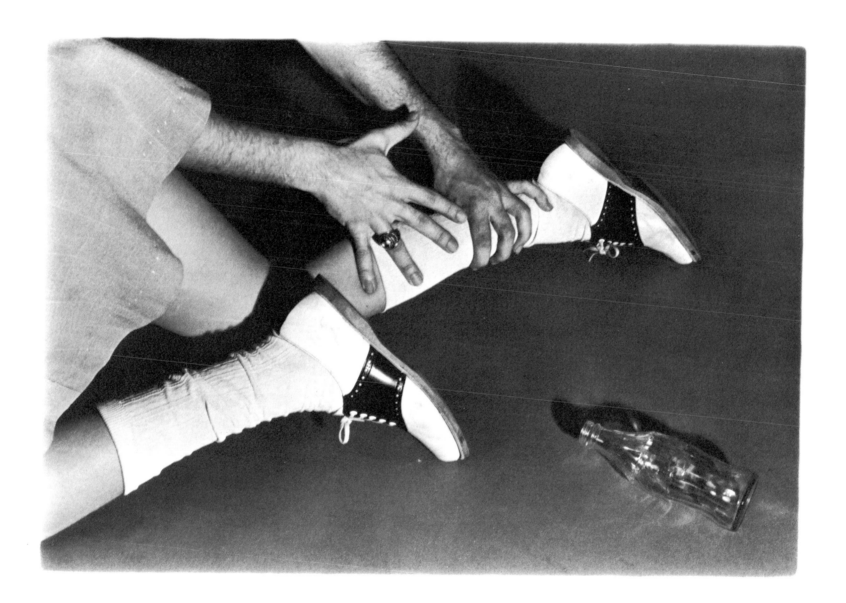

When her mother first noticed a red stain on her panties and roared, "You're a woman now", she promptly fainted.

She developed slowly but learned how to stuff her bra so that both sides matched.

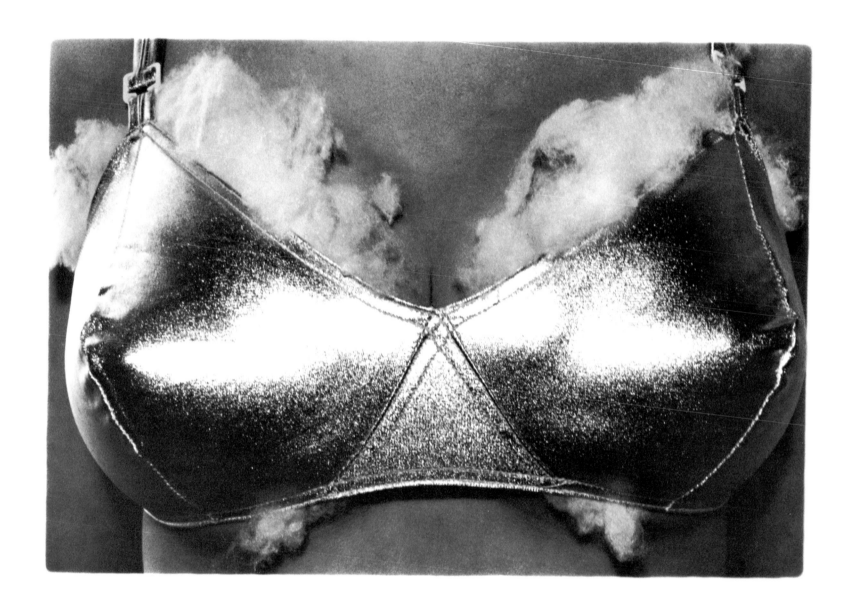

She scotch-taped her nose up before dates hoping it would stay that way.

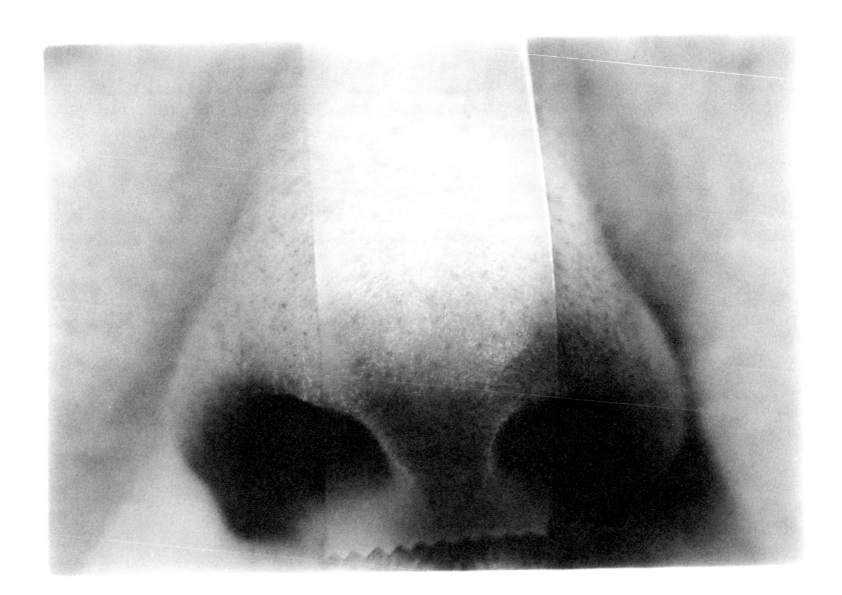

In order to be fasionably thin she would crash diet
though she was warned it would be curtains for her stomach.

She was told that her eyes were her greatest asset.

For fear of being a wallflower at dances, she would dress up in striking outfits.

She inevitably ran her nylons immediately after putting them on.

Loves me, loves me not, loves me ...
she would demolish rose after rose until it came out right.

She would demurely sip cherry Kool Aid from a wine glass and puff on bubble gum cigarettes.

She imagined herself a starlet.

They were continually telling her that she had stars in her eyes.

Looking at her books upside down, she exercised both her mind and her body.

She always read the endings of books before the beginnings.

Fin